SBN 11 290111 5

Cover: *Telescope by Christopher Cock* (see Plate 3)

A Science Museum
illustrated booklet

ASTRONOMY

2: Astronomical Telescopes

by A. G. Thoday,
B.Sc., A.R.C.S.

Her Majesty's Stationery
Office, London 1971

Introduction

The telescope was discovered by accident in 1608, and it is generally accepted that the discoverer was the spectacle maker Hans Lippershey of Middelburg on the island of Walcheren. He found, by chance, that with two convex lenses held apart he was able to see the church spire appear much larger and he promptly constructed a telescope with two such lenses mounted in a tube which he then presented to the States-General, Prince Maurice.

The news of this discovery soon spread throughout Europe, reaching Galileo Galilei in Venice in May 1609. After only a day's study of the optics involved he designed the now well-known *Galilean* telescope. This consisted of a plano-convex object-glass and a plano-concave eyepiece mounted in a lead tube.

Galileo lost no time in constructing improved telescopes with greater magnifications and applying them to his astronomical studies. By the following year he had observed the nature of the Moon's surface, discovered four satellites of the planet Jupiter and seen the planet Venus appear crescent shaped, resembling the Moon during its first quarter. In addition he observed sunspots and noted that they changed position from day to day, indicating that the Sun revolved about an axis.

The images seen through telescopes in those days were of very limited quality on three accounts, namely the quality of the glass, spherical aberration and chromatic aberration. Spherical aberration results from light passing through different parts of the lens being brought to a focus at varying distances from the lens. Chromatic aberration is produced by light of the different spectral colours being refracted by different amounts on passing through the lens. Astronomers and telescope makers found by experience that by reducing the curvature of the object-glass, and thereby increasing its focal length, the effects of both spherical and chromatic aberration were reduced. This resulted in a phase, during the middle of the 17th century, when telescopes were increased progressively in length, culminating in the 150-foot telescope by Hevelius of Danzig and the aerial telescope by Christian Huygens.

Isaac Newton showed that white light was composed of what are now known as the colours of the spectrum, and concluded that it was not possible to obtain lenses which would be free from chromatic aberration. He therefore turned his attention to mirrors and made his first telescope of this form in 1668. James Gregory had anticipated Newton by proposing the use of concave mirrors for telescopes in 1663, but the proposal was never put into practice.

Newtonian Telescope

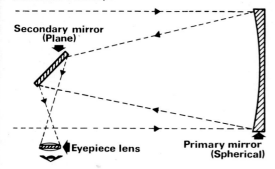

**Secondary mirror
(Plane)**

Eyepiece lens

**Primary mirror
(Spherical)**

All mirrors up to the middle of the 19th century were made of metal, usually alloys: they gave a high polish, but often failed to retain it for long periods, thus necessitating repolishing. Newton used an alloy known as bell-metal which consisted of six parts copper to two parts tin. Later speculum metal was used.

Telescopes which have lenses are known as *refractors*, and those with mirrors as *reflectors*, though both types incorporate lenses in the eyepieces.

In 1672 the Frenchman Cassegrain proposed another form of the reflecting telescope, with a convex secondary mirror. As these types of reflecting telescopes are the basis of the modern telescope it is appropriate to indicate their form.

Gregorian Telescope

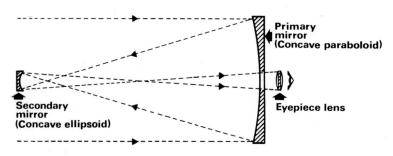

Cassegrain Telescope

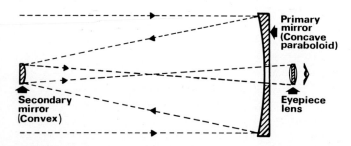

The quality of these early reflecting telescopes depended largely upon the skill of a few opticians and their ability to grind the necessary mirrors. Between 1737 and 1768 James Short was the outstanding telescope maker and the majority of his telescopes were of Gregorian form.

In the second half of the 18th century, the refracting telescope steadily came back into favour. This was largely the result of the work of John Dollond who produced the first achromatic objectglasses. They consisted of two lenses—a concave one of flint glass and a convex one of crown glass; this combination greatly reduced chromatic aberration. Chester Moor Hall first proposed this method in 1729. John Dollond patented his invention in 1758, but he died three years later and it was his son, Peter Dollond, who really popularised the refracting telescope again. The triple lens objectglass was first produced in 1763, and from that date onwards the refracting telescope increased in popularity although improvements in the quality and size of object-glasses were slow. Towards the end of the century, Guinand in Switzerland found the secret of obtaining improved glass discs. He went to Munich in 1805 where he trained Joseph Fraunhofer, who did much to popularise the refracting telescope by incorporating lenses made from these discs. As a result, refractors became more popular than reflectors during the first half and more of the 19th century.

In 1773 William Herschel, who was the Director of Music at Bath, started to take a serious interest in astronomy, not only as an observer but also in making his own telescopes. These were Newtonian reflectors of speculum metal, 71% copper and 29% tin, which he cast and polished himself. He was soon making the best astronomical telescopes in Europe and selling them in increasing numbers, while assiduously continuing his astronomical observations. In 1778 he made a 7-foot focal length Newtonian with a mirror of 6.2 inch aperture, and with it he made history by observing on 13 March 1781 a new planet now known as Uranus. In 1782 George III appointed Herschel his Royal Astronomer and this enabled him to relinquish his post in Bath and give his full time to astronomical observations and telescope construction. In 1789 he made a telescope of aperture 48-inch with a focal length of 40 feet which was at that time the world's largest telescope and remained so until Lord Rosse completed his 6-foot speculum in 1845.

During the second half of the 19th century the silver-on-glass disc replaced the speculum metal disc, and this led to the reflector regaining popularity. Today practically all large telescopes are reflectors with a Pyrex or fused silica disc having a reflecting surface of aluminium.

In general the form of mounting of astronomical telescopes can be separated into three groups, viz. *equatorial*, *transit* and *altazimuth*. By far the most popular form is the equatorial mounting. In this mounting the telescope is supported on an arm which is parallel to the polar axis, that is the axis of revolution of the Earth. As this arm, usually referred to as the polar axis, rotates so the telescope sweeps over a parallel of declination. When once the telescope has been set to observe a star it is only necessary to rotate this arm for the star to be kept in the field of view. With large telescopes the polar axis is rotated by a clockwork mechanism at a rate equal to the Earth's rotation, but in the contrary direction, so that once the telescope has been sighted on a star it will continue to follow that star automatically. This is essential in photographic work and especially when observing faint stars. The first transit mounting is credited to O. Römer of Copenhagen, in 1684, and is used today only in observatories for measuring the right ascension and declination of a star and for time checks on known stars. In the transit instrument the axis of the telescope can only move in the vertical plane through the meridian. In the altazimuth mounting the telescope can be moved in two orthogonal directions, in azimuth and elevation, but normally it cannot be operated so as to follow a star automatically. Early refractors and later portable instruments were often mounted in this manner, but it has seldom been adopted for large astronomical telescopes, two exceptions are Nasmyth's 20-inch reflector and the world's largest telescope at present being erected in Russia. Today all large telescopes are reflectors, the largest in this country being the Isaac Newton telescope at the Royal Greenwich Observatory, Herstmonceux, with a 98-inch reflector. In America the largest is the Hale telescope at Mount Palomar, Southern California, with a 200-inch disc, while the world's largest reflector now being erected in the Caucasian Mountains is of 6 metres diameter.

Many early telescopes were defined by their focal lengths, but as the size of the object-glass or primary mirror increased it has become the universal practice to give the diameter of this and not its focal length. The accepted description of the telescope at the time of its construction has been adopted in this booklet.

The astronomical telescopes and models illustrated and described in this booklet are from the Astronomy Collection and cover the period from the discovery of the telescope up to the end of the 19th century.

1 Copies of telescopes made by Galileo

In the summer of 1609 Galileo Galilei, known today as Galileo, heard 'that a certain Fleming had constructed a spyglass by means of which visible objects, though very distant from the eye of the observer, were distinctly seen as if nearby'. A few days later he received a similar report from Paris; he immediately applied the theory of refraction to the problem and succeeded in inventing his telescope within the following 24 hours.

This form of telescope, with convex lens object-glass and concave lens eyepiece is known today as the *Galilean Telescope*, an arrangement still used in opera-glasses.

Galileo immediately turned his telescopes to the sky, and the study of Astronomy took a fresh and important turn. He saw the surface features of the Moon, the phases of the planet Venus and four satellites of Jupiter. All these observations supported the Copernican system.

Both his telescopes and his observations were described by Galileo in his book *Siderius Nuncius*—Starry Messenger—which was published less than a year later, in the spring of 1610.

Here are shown copies of two telescopes made by Galileo; the originals are preserved in the Museo di Storia della Scienza in Florence. The tube of the longer one is made of wood and covered with paper, the double-convex object-glass has a focal length of 132.7 cm. while the eyepiece lens is plano-concave, giving a magnification of 14. The smaller tube is made of paper and covered with dark red leather, with a double-convex object-glass of focal length 95.6 cm. and a double-concave ocular, giving a magnification of 20.

The vignette shows a copy of the protrait of Galileo by Guido Sustermans, painted in 1635 when the sitter was 71. The original is now in the Uffizi Gallery, Florence.

2 Copy of Newton's reflecting telescope

The first person to make a reflecting telescope was Sir Isaac Newton in 1668. He replaced the object-glass by a concave mirror or speculum; this idea had previously been suggested by several persons, including James Gregory in 1663.

Newton turned his attention to the reflecting telescope following his experiments on the refraction and dispersion of light through glass prisms. He concluded that lenses would always produce chromatic aberration, so the resulting images would always have coloured edges.

In 1671 he made a second telescope which is still preserved in the rooms of the Royal Society, the illustration is a copy of this second telescope. The concave reflector is of bell metal, an alloy consisting of six parts copper to two parts tin. The mirror readily tarnished and required frequent repolishing, and even when polished a large percentage of the incoming light was absorbed by the mirror, thus giving a dull image. Light from the concave mirror is reflected by a plane mirror into the eyepiece in the side of the tube, the eyepiece is a very small convex lens. The magnification of the whole system is about 25.

3   Telescope by Christopher Cock

This is the oldest complete telescope in the Science Museum; it is signed—Christopher Cock, Londini. 1673. The aperture of the object-glass, which is a double convex lens, is 2.2 cm. and its focal length is 91 cm. The eyepiece system, which contains three double convex lenses, is of the type devised by von Schyrle de Rheita in 1645 and gives a magnification of about 14. The image seen through the eyepiece is therefore an erect one and today such a telescope is regarded as a terrestrial one, but that distinction was not made in the 17th century.

There are five draw-tubes made of paper and covered with white vellum, and when fully extended the telescope is about 4 ft. 6½ in. in length.

Christopher Cock was one of the two leading optic-glass grinders in London during the second half of the 17th century; the other was Richard Reeves. Cock made Hooke's compound microscope in about 1665 and was commissioned by the Royal Society to make various telescopes, including a larger copy of Newton's telescope.

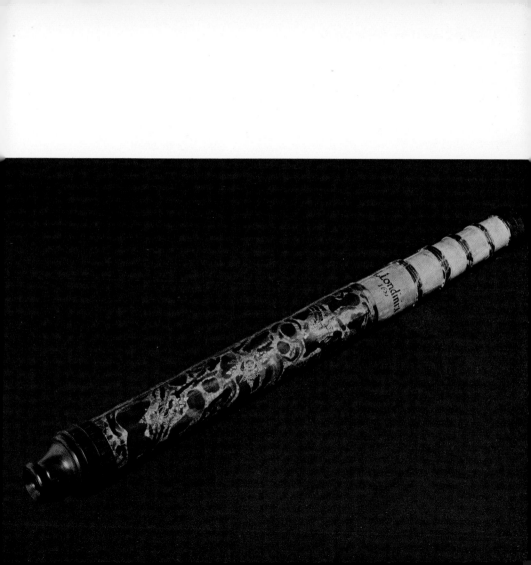

4   Early portable telescopes

Johannes Kepler in his book *Dioptrice*, published in 1611, suggested the use of an eyepiece with a convex lens; this would give a larger field of view, but an inverted image. In about 1645 Schyrle of Bohemia introduced an additional convex lens into such an eyepiece, thus giving an erect image.

To obtain larger images it was necessary to make object-glasses of greater focal length, and at the same time an added advantage resulted, in that spherical and chromatic aberration were less noticeable, particularly if the lens was stopped down. So from the middle of the 17th century telescopes became longer and an increasing number of draw-tubes were introduced to reduce the size of the telescope for portability.

The small telescope illustrated is of Italian origin with the object-glass engraved *Pietro Patroni in Milano*, so it can be dated between 1714 and 1722 when Patroni flourished as an optician in Milan. There are five draw-tubes which give a length of over three feet to the telescope when it is extended, though when closed its length is less than 11 inches. The eyepiece contains three convex lenses.

The larger telescope is English and dates from early in the 18th century. When closed its length is about 4 ft. 10 in., but when extended, $16\frac{1}{2}$ ft., all the tubes are of wood. There is a double object glass, one marked 'day' and the other 'night'. When used with the night object glass for astronomical work the erector lens system is removed leaving a single double convex lens in the eyepiece.

The telescope on the stand is Italian and of the same period. All the tubes are made of parchment, the six draw-tubes being covered with green paper. When closed it measures about 18 in. but when extended, over six ft. The object glass is plano-convex, and the eyepiece system is composed of three convex lenses.

5 Huygens' aerial telescope

The second half of the 17th century was the era of very long telescopes, now known as *aerial telescopes*, with which are associated the names of Johannes Hevelius of Danzig (1611-1687) and Christian Huygens of Holland (1629-1695).

Hevelius first made telescopes of 60 ft. and 70 ft. in length, and finally one of 150 ft. The 'tube' was made of sections, each of which was formed by two wooden planks at right angles, so forming a two-sided trough. The object-glass was fixed at one end and the eyepiece at the other. The 'tube' or trough was attached to a high pole by ropes, and raised or lowered, as required, by assistants.

Huygens' aerial telescope consisted of an object-glass fixed into a metal tube and mounted on a stand on a high mast. This stand could be raised or lowered as required and was balanced by a counterpoise weight. The eyepiece was also mounted in a metal tube and held in the hand or supported on a stand. The only connection between the eyepiece and the object-glass was a taut silk line.

Many such aerial telescopes of focal lengths between 122 ft. and 210 ft. were made by Huygens. They were the best, for the purpose of astronomical observations, for over 50 years but they were not suitable for angular measurements. It was with such a telescope that the first satellite of Saturn was discovered, by Huygens in 1655. Shown here is the objective cell and eyepiece of his 210 ft. focal length aerial telescope which was presented to the Royal Society. The drawing, illustrating the manner of mounting and operating the telescope is taken from *A Compleat System of Opticks* by Robert Smith 1738. The lantern shown in the drawing was used to illuminate the object-glass on a dark night, so that the star could be rapidly picked up.

6   The first Gregorian telescope

James Gregory of Aberdeen, in his book *Optica Promota*, published in 1663, proposed the first reflecting telescope with two concave mirrors, the collector being paraboloidal with a small ellipsoidal reflector which focussed the image at the centre of the main speculum in which there was a small circular aperature to allow the light to pass to the eyepiece. Gregory commissioned two London opticians to make the reflectors, but he was not satisfied with the results and pressed his ideas no further.

It was Isaac Newton who produced the first reflecting telescope of his own design, in 1668. This was a small telescope and over 50 years later, in about 1719, John Hadley made a larger and better example which he showed to the Royal Society in January 1721. Hadley continued to work on the grinding of mirrors and succeeded in producing the first successful example of a *Gregorian telescope* in 1726. This is the telescope illustrated here and remained with the Hadley family until 1874.

The main collector of light, corresponding to the object glass of refracting telescopes, is a 2 in. concave speculum, the composition of which was not disclosed by Hadley. It contains a small circular aperture through which the light passed into the eyepiece, after reflection from a concave reflector. This eyepiece is of the Keplian form with two plano-convex lenses. The total length of the telescope is about 14 in.

John Hadley, who subsequently became a Vice-President of the Royal Society, is probably better known as the inventor of the reflecting octant in 1731. Later this was developed into the sextant and has been a boon to navigators ever since.

7 Gregorian telescope by George Adams

Following John Hadley's success in making a Gregorian telescope, London opticians soon turned their attention to the making of such instruments. The general pattern, in all respects, was very similar to this fine example of the work of George Adams, the elder, and dates from about 1740. This style of Gregorian telescope changed very little throughout the remainder of the 18th century.

The main speculum mirror is $2\frac{3}{4}$ in. in diameter, with a focal length of 12 in. and the eyepiece gives a magnification of 40 with a field of view of $0.°5$. The secondary speculum can be adjusted at the eyepiece by means of the rod, visible along the side of the tube. The tube is covered with red shagreen.

George Adams was appointed instrument maker to the Prince of Wales before the latter's accession as George III in 1760 and continued as instrument maker to the King until his death in 1772, when he was succeeded in the business and the royal appointment by his son George Adams, the younger.

8 Equatorially mounted reflector by James Short

James Short (1710-68) was the outstanding telescope maker of his day and specialised in the making of reflectors. His speculum mirrors were of outstanding quality, but his methods of producing these specula and the grinding of them were never disclosed.

Here is an example of one of his largest telescopes, mounted as an equatorial. The main speculum is 9 in. in diameter and has a focal length of 49 in. There are secondary specula which enable the telescope to be used in either Gregorian, Cassegrainian or Newtonian form. In addition there are three eyepieces by which magnifications of about 100 to 400 can be obtained. The equatorial circle is graduated in hours with sub-divisions to 2 minutes, while the declination scale can be read to 2 minutes of arc.

James Short had an unusual way of inscribing his telescopes; this one, for example, bears the following (around the eyepiece) at the base of the telescope, *James Short London* $\frac{no\ 6}{1364}$ *49*. The 49 indicates the focal length of the telescope, No 6 indicates the number of telescopes made of this size, while 1364 is the serial number of all the telescopes he made to that date. The highest serial number known is 1370 and as he died in June 1768 it is probable that this telescope was made in 1767 or early 1768.

James Short was born in Edinburgh and started to make telescopes there immediately after taking his M.A. at the University. His exceptional skill soon became known and in 1736, at the age of 26, he moved to London. At the time of his death he was much involved in the preparations for the various expeditions which were going to be deployed around the world to observe the Transit of Venus in 1769. It was for this purpose that James Cook was sent on his first expedition to the South Seas in 1768.

9   Herschel's 7-foot Newtonian reflector

William Herschel, born in Hanover in 1738, started life as a musician in the Hanoverian Guards at the age of 14. He came to England when he was 19 years of age and in 1766 was appointed organist of the Octagon chapel in Bath. He started to study mathematics and astronomy in his spare time and in the summer of 1773 bought instruments, including telescopes, to observe the heavens. Finding them unsatisfactory for his purpose he set about constructing his own instruments. In 1774 he made a $5\frac{1}{2}$ ft. Gregorian telescope and the following year saw him produce his first Newtonian reflector. He made, ground and polished his own specula in his spare time. On 13 March 1781 he observed a faint star which he thought was either a comet or a nebula, but which turned out to be a new planet which he called Georgium Sidus, but we now know it as the planet Uranus.

After his fame had become established as an astronomer Herschel was given an appointment as Royal Astronomer to George III, in 1782. He moved from Bath to Datchet in 1782 and to Slough in 1786, where he remained until his death in 1822. He supplemented his income by making telescopes for sale, many like the example illustrated here, which probably dates from about 1785.

This 7-ft. Newtonian reflector has a speculum mirror of $6\frac{1}{4}$ in. diameter with a focal length of 7 ft. 4 in. The tube is hexagonal in corss-section and made of mahogany.

While at Slough Herschel rose to become the greatest astronomer of his time. He specialised in the study of double stars, star clusters and nebulae. He also continued to make larger telescopes, a 20-ft. reflector with an 18.8 in. aperture and finally a 40-ft. reflector of 48 in. aperture, which was the largest telescope in the world in 1789.

10　Portable equatorial by Ramsden

This instrument is a portable equatorially mounted Cassegrain type telescope, made by Jesse Ramsden of London in the early 1790s. Although portable it is a rigid and heavily constructed form of English mounting, introduced by Ramsden. The polar axis is normally set for about 52°, but can be adjusted by means of the screw, seen at its foot, over a range of 5°, so this instrument can be used for places of latitude between about 50° and 54°. The declination scale, which reads zero when the telescope axis is at right angles to the polar axis, extends from a depression of over 50° to an elevation of 60°, and with the vernier can be read to one minute of arc. The equatorial scale is graduated in hours which are subdivided into two minutes of time; this scale can be read with the vernier to one second of time.

The telescope when once locked on to a star can follow that star by simply rotating the telescope about the polar axis.

The main collecting mirror of the telescope is a 6 in. aperture concave mirror of speculum metal, with a central circular aperture of $1\frac{1}{4}$ in. diameter for the reflected rays from the secondary convex mirror to pass into the eyepiece. These rays can be focussed on the eyepiece, which consists of two plano-convex lenses, by adjusting the position of this secondary mirror using an adjusting rod. The head of the latter is near the eyepiece, but on the opposite side of the telescope in this illustration.

There is a sighting refracting telescope fitted on the upper surface of the telescope tube.

Jesse Ramsden (1735-1800) worked for such well-known instrument makers as Sisson, Adams and Dollond before starting on his own in 1762. He rose to become the outstanding instrument maker of his day, not only in this country, but throughout Europe.

11 Refracting telescope by Tulley

Even after John Dollond's patent for achromatic lenses became void in 1772 opticians were slow to make such glasses for refracting telescopes. This resulted from their lack of experience in such work, the difficulty in obtaining blanks of flint glass free from flaws, and the high import duty on such blanks.

Peter Dollond was the outstanding maker of such telescopes until his death in 1820, when Charles Tulley took over that rôle.

This refractor, with achromatic object-glass, was made by Tulley in 1822 and is a very good example of the best quality of such glasses at that time. The aperture of the object-glass is $3\frac{3}{16}$ in. and its focal length about 45 in. The brass tube of the telescope is made in two parts which screw together, and with the eyepiece tube has a length of 56 in. A number of eyepieces give magnifications ranging from 70 to 122.

The mounting was designed either for table mounting in a house, for observation through an open window, or for a stand in the open, as illustrated here.

Charles Tulley started business as an optician in Islington about 1782 and rose to become the leading telescope maker of his time; he died in October 1830. He took his two sons, William and Thomas, into the business which they continued after their father's death.

12   Achromatic refractor by W. & S. Jones

This telescope, made about 1828, is typical of those made during the first half of the 19th century for the wealthy amateur observer. The object-glass of the refractor, composed of two lenses, is $3\frac{1}{4}$ in. in diameter, with a focal length of 4 ft. A number of eyepieces give varying magnifications from 98 to 220.

The brass tube is slightly tapered from the object-glass end and is supported on a solid brass tripod table stand. There are steadying rods both front and back with a rack and screw in the back rod for adjusting the elevation of the telescope; the extent of this elevation is indicated by a clinometer under the forward part of the tube. The telescope can be rotated in azimuth by means of a tangent screw with Hooke's universal joint to which is attached an arm (not shown in illustration) so that the observer could train the telescope while still observing. The small telescope on the tube is a sighting telescope of low magnification.

The brothers W. & S. Jones were in business as opticians at Holborn, London, from 1793, continuing the business founded by their father, John Jones. William Jones died in 1831 and his brother Samuel survived him; the firm continued until 1860.

13 The Shuckburgh equatorial

The construction of this telescope marked the beginning of an era of large equatorial refractors built for private observatories. This telescope, made by Jesse Ramsden for Sir George Shuckburgh in 1791, was the largest refractor of its time, and the mounting was the first of the type now known as *Old English* or *Double Yoke*.

The object-glass is an achromatic double lens of 4.2 in. aperture, with a focal length of 65 in., while various eyepieces could give magnifications between 60 and 550.

The scales on the equatorial and declination circles were divided by Matthew Berge, the head workman to Jesse Ramsden. It was Berge who succeeded to the business on Ramsden's death.

Sir George Shuckburgh had the telescope erected in his private observatory at Shuckburgh in Warwickshire and seven years after his death in 1804 his heir C. C. C. Jenkinson, later 3rd Earl of Liverpool, presented it to the Royal Observatory, Greenwich where it remained until 1929.

The equatorial scale was re-divided by Troughton & Simms in 1860. While still at Greenwich various modifications were also made to the base of the polar axis and the supports for the equatorial ring. The illustration shows how the telescope appeared after these modifications had been carried out.

14   Portable transit telescope

The transit telescope was set up with its axis in the plane of the meridian and used to observe the passage of heavenly bodies across the meridian. The purpose of the instrument was the determination of declination and right ascension of heavenly bodies as well as for time-checking, using stars whose positions were accurately known.

This portable transit telescope was made by Troughton and Simms in the second quarter of the 19th century. The aperture of the object-glass is $2\frac{1}{2}$ in. and its focal length 2 ft.; at its principal focus is a diaphragm carrying cross-wires which were illuminated at night by light from a lamp. The light passed down the hollow axle of the telescope and was reflected down the tube to illuminate the cross-wires by a small inclined metal mirror of $\frac{1}{8}$ in. diameter.

In addition to its astronomical uses this transit instrument could be used by geodetic engineers and surveyors in tunnelling and mining operations. For this reason there is a hole in the base frame so that the telescope could be used to view vertically downwards.

15 The Smyth equatorial

This was the first equatorially mounted telescope in this country to be driven by clock-work. It was initially erected in 1829, by Admiral W. H. Smyth in his private observatory at Bedford. In 1840 it was acquired by Dr John Lee and set up in his observatory at Hartwell, and subsequently it was purchased by the British Government for use in observing the Transit of Venus, in 1874.

Of especial interest is the achromatic object-glass which was made by Charles Tulley of Islington and was regarded as his 'chef d'oeuvre'; even when it was tested in 1929, 100 years after Tulley made it, it was considered first class by the standards of that time. The aperture of the lens is 5.8 in. and its focal length $8\frac{1}{2}$ ft. The flint blank for this achromatic lens was obtained from Paris by Sir James South in 1828.

The instrument, together with the driving clock, was designed by Rev. R. Sheepshanks, and the construction was carried out by George Dollond who also made the eyepieces which afford a range of magnification from 22 to 1200. The driving clock was made by C. May.

The counterpoise for the telescope and declination circle on the mahogany polar axis was a lead weight which can be seen on the right-hand side of this axis.

With this telescope Admiral Smyth made observations of 580 double stars, 20 binary, 80 triple stars, multiple star clusters and nebulae; these observations were recorded in the Bedford Catalogue which formed the second volume of his book *Cycle of Celestial Objects* which was published in 1844. Smyth continued to use this telescope after it was transferred to Hartwell, and made observations with it until 1859; his results are recorded in his book *Speculum Hartwellianum*, published in 1860.

16 Nasmyth's 20-inch reflector

James Nasmyth was a Scottish engineer, famous for his invention of the steam hammer; concurrently with his engineering activities, he was a keen amateur astronomer who constructed his own telescopes.

The telescope illustrated here was designed and made by him in 1842 and used, first at Patricroft near Manchester, and from 1856, at Penshurst, Kent. Made of speculum metal, the 20 in. reflector has a focal length of about 14 ft., and was usually used as a Cassegrain, though it could be used as a Newtonian reflector.

There are two unusual features of this telescope, the altazimuth mounting and the eyepiece arrangement which enabled the observer to remain seated without moving his eye while the telescope could be pointed to any part of the sky.

The sheet-iron tube is mounted on two hollow trunnions supported on two rigid triangular uprights secured to a turn-table base. The observer's seat is also fixed to this base, with the control handles for training and elevating the telescope close at hand.

When used in the Cassegrain form, the light beam from the main mirror was reflected back down the tube by a $4\frac{1}{2}$ in. convex reflector, situated at the upper end of the tube, to an elliptical plane mirror inclined at 45° to the tube's axis, which directed the beam through the hollow trunnion to the eyepiece fitted at its end.

Nasmyth's main work with this telescope was his study of the Sun and the lunar surface. He made detailed sketches of the Moon's surface and from them constructed plaster casts which he photographed in sunlight, faithfully reproducing the lunar effects of light and shadow. From these he developed his volcanic theory of the formation of lunar craters, this is illustrated in *The Moon* by James Nasmyth and James Carpenter, published in 1871.

17 Model of the Rosse telescope

The Rosse telescope, known as the Leviathan of Parsonstown, was the largest telescope in the world at the time of its completion in 1845. It was not until 1919 that a larger one was completed, the 100-inch telescope at Mount Wilson, California.

The Rosse telescope was designed and made by William Parsons, third Earl of Rosse, and erected at Birr Castle near the village of Parsonstown in Central Ireland. The main problem was in the construction of the large speculum mirror which was 6 ft. in diameter and when completed had a focal length of 53 ft. It was used as a Newtonian reflector. The mirror was held in a wooden box hinged to the masonry in the ground. The tube was made of thick deal staves held together with iron clamp rings; it was raised or lowered by means of chains, attached to its upper end, and these chains passed around a windlass which was operated by two workmen. The tube could therefore be elevated from an almost horizontal position through the zenith to the pole. Its lateral movement was greatly restricted by the masonry walls and could only be moved through about 1 hour of Right Ascension.

This large telescope was mainly used for observing the lunar scenery, planets and nebulae. Its great light-gathering power together with the resolving power of the eyepieces showed that many celestial objects previously thought to be nebulae were in fact clusters of stars.

Its use was greatly restricted by its site, since the frequent cloudy weather and the presence of mists from the neighbouring Bog of Allen limited its use. The telescope was dismantled in 1908; much of the masonry still remains at Birr Castle, but the mirror is now preserved in the Science Museum.

18 The Oxford Heliometer

The Oxford Heliometer is so-called because it was constructed for the Radcliffe Observatory, Oxford and the $7\frac{1}{2}$ in. aperture object-glass is a divided one. Although this type of object-glass is known as a micrometer in this country (cf Dollond's Divided Object-glass Micrometer) it is usually known on the continent as a heliometer. This is a large equatorially mounted telescope, the mounting being of the German form. The telescope parts and mounting were made by A. & G. Repsold of Hamburg and the object-glass by G. Merz & Sons of Munich. Although the instrument was ordered in 1840 it was not completed until 1848 and the building to house it was not completed until the end of 1849.

The divided object-glass is an uncemented achromatic doublet of $7\frac{1}{2}$ in. aperture, with a focal length of $10\frac{1}{2}$ ft. The semi-lenses are mounted in cylindrical slides, curved in the direction of the micrometer's length with a radius of curvature equal to the focal length of the object-glass; by this arrangement the separation of the component half-lenses does not affect the definition in the eyepieces. This was the first astronomical instrument in which electricity was used to illuminate the scales; current from a battery passed through a thin platinum wire which was raised to incandescence and illuminated the scales at the objective end; these scales could then be read by a low-power micrometer microscope at the eyepiece end. Not only was this heliometer the largest in this country, but also it was the most powerful instrument of its type in the world for over 20 years. The very accurate micrometer was used for measuring the angular separation of stars and the angular diameters of other heavenly bodies.

An unusual and noticeable feature of the instrument is the large telescope tube of hammered brass which is bright and lacquered, not painted.

19   Model of Loewy's coudé equatorial

During the 19th century equatorial refractors became increasingly popular and their sizes steadily increased, but this brought in its wake problems of stability, convenience of observing and size of observatory and dome.

To overcome these difficulties, M. Loewy of the Paris Observatory. designed this coudé (Fr. bent, angled) equatorial which had the following advantages over the conventional equatorial:

1. Greater stability, and the ability to measure larger angles than was usually possible with an ordinary equatorial.

2. The eyepiece of the telescope remained in virtually a fixed position.

3. A simple shed on wheels to cover the telescope instead of an expensive dome.

The object-glass, of about 10 in. aperture, is contained in the box-like structure on the right; below it is a hollow tube at right-angles to the polar axis, also hollow. Light from the heavenly body is reflected through the object-glass by a plane mirror at an angle of 45° to the axis of the mirror and tube; there is another plane mirror at the junction of this tube with the polar axis which reflects the light into the eyepiece at the upper end of the polar axis.

The fixed eyepiece enabled the observer to work in a more comfortable position from where all the movements of the telescope would be controlled and reading taken. The polar axis was rotated by means of a motor below the observing position, while the plane mirror in front of the object-glass could be rotated from the observing position to allow for the correct declination of the observed body.

This telescope was constructed for the Paris Observatory and completed in 1882, a similar though larger one was built for the same observatory in 1890.

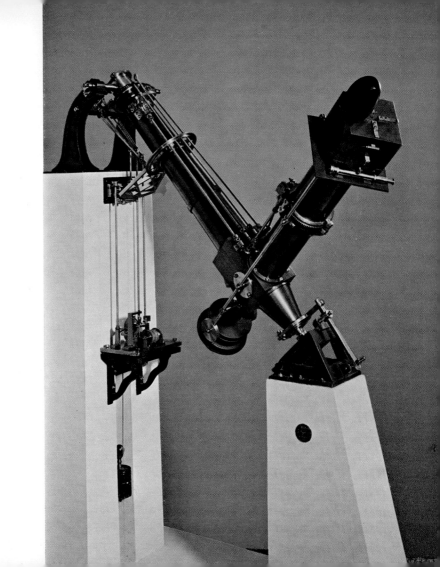

20   Isaac Roberts' equatorially mounted telescopes

Isaac Roberts first became interested in Astronomy in his 50th year in 1878, when he purchased a 7 in. refractor from T. Cooke and Sons of York. He built his own observatory at Maghull, near Liverpool, in 1883 and began experimenting in the photography of stars, using dry plates. As a result of these experiments he ordered a 20-inch silver-on-glass reflector from Sir Howard Grubb of Dublin. This 20-inch reflector, of focal length 100 inches, was mounted equatorially on the same mounting with his 7-inch refractor. This mounting is generally referred to as the German form, and was popular during the latter part of the 19th century, but here the refractor acts as the counterpoise for the larger reflector.

A weight driven clockwork mechanism, controlled by a governor, rotated the twin mounting around the polar axis at the same rate as the Earth's rotation, so that the stars were kept continuously in the field of view of the telescopes. Though they move together in Right Ascension they have independent adjustments for Declination so that they can be used separately.

The 20-inch reflector was mounted by April, 1885 but adjustments were necessary and photography of the stars did not commence until the following year. In October 1887 a photograph taken by Roberts with this telescope showed, for the first time, the spiral form of the great nebula in Andromeda.

The twin mounting was moved in 1890 to a new observatory on Crowhurst Hill in Sussex, and here Roberts, now retired from business, gave his whole time to the photography of stars, star clusters and nebulae.

These telescopes were used for a short period at the Royal Greenwich Observatory and are now assembled, in working order, in the Observatory on the roof of the Museum.

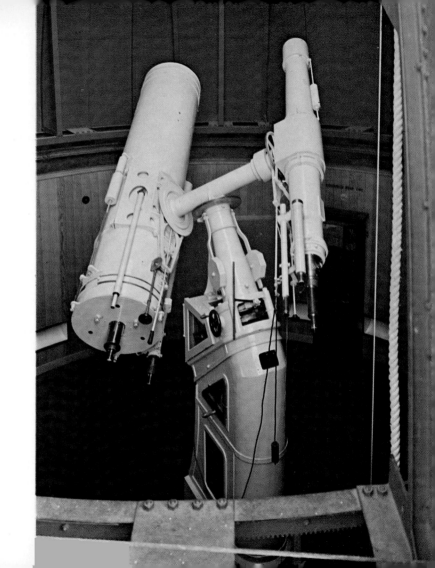

Science Museum illustrated booklets

Other titles in this series:

Published by
Her Majesty's Stationery Office
and obtainable from the
Government Bookshops listed
on cover page iv (post orders
to PO Box 569 London SE1)

35p each (by post 37½p)

Printed in England for
Her Majesty's Stationery Office
by W. Heffer & Sons Ltd
Cambridge

Dd. 502189 K64